For Richard,
Max and Molly
C.H.

For Georgia
H.M.

First published 1996
by Walker Books Ltd
87 Vauxhall Walk, London SE11 5HJ

Text © 1996 Heather Maisner
Illustrations © 1996 Charlotte Hard

2 4 6 8 10 9 7 5 3 1

Printed in Hong Kong

This book has been typeset in Providence

British Library Cataloguing in Publication Data
A catalogue record for this title is available
from the British Library.

ISBN 0-7445-3743-6

SAVE BRAVE TED

written by
Heather Maisner

illustrated by
Charlotte Hard

WALKER BOOKS
AND SUBSIDIARIES
LONDON · BOSTON · SYDNEY

HELP! My name is Brave Ted. My eight friends and I are toys and we were stolen by Mighty Monster. He wanted us as presents for the horrid mini-monsters who live at the top of Monster Mountain.

We cut a hole in Monster's bag to see which way he went.

Whenever Monster stopped for a rest, one of us got out and hid. And we put something heavy in the bag instead.

When we reached Monster Mountain, the bag was full, but I was the only toy left. Monster was furious! He blew icy flames and locked me up.

I've written down Monster's route for you. Please come and rescue us!

- Follow the route to Monster Mountain.

- Find a toy hiding wherever Monster stopped to sleep.

- Rescue me. Then take us all back home.

Come quickly! Monster says he may go back and look for the missing toys.

Brave Ted

P.S. I gave this message to Big Brown Bird, who flew with it to you.

Start at the
ruined church.

Go down the
cobbled path,

Past the children
with a kite,

Round the pond with
ducks and swans,

Through the yellow
painted gate,

Behind the row
of smiling cows.

Stop at the
basket of apples.

Monster went to sleep here.
Herbie ran off and hid.
We put some apples in the bag.

Can you
find Herbie?

Now you are going to the forest.

Start at the place
where three fox cubs sit.

Step over two giant
spotted toadstools,

Go round the bushes
with red berries,

To the house with
blue windows,

Past a tree where owls live,

Between two rows
of beehives,

Along the leafy path.

Stop at the pile of logs.

**Monster went to sleep here.
Snake slid off and hid.
We put a log in the bag.**

**Can you
find Snake?**

Now you are going to the zoo.

Start at the blue arch.

Go past the snake with
a bunch of balloons,

Up to the bridge,

Over the pool where
penguins play,

In front of the hippos
in their pond,

Between two stripy tigers,

Under the trees
where parrots fly.

Stop at the wheelbarrow
full of bricks.

**Monster went to sleep here.
Percy ran off and hid.
We put a brick in the bag.**

**Can you
find Percy?**

Now you are going to the desert.

Start by the woman
in a dark blue dress.

Go behind a big fish
spraying water,

In front of a man
selling brushes,

Over a large tortoise,

Round a man charming
a snake,

To a tall prickly cactus,

Past the trees where
camels stand.

Stop at the banana tree.

**Monster went to sleep here.
Rosie ran off and hid.
We put some bananas in the bag.**

**Can you
find Rosie?**

Now you are going to the fair.

Start by the clown in spotted trousers.

Go under the rollercoaster snake,

To the crazy mirror,

Round the fortune-teller's tent,

In front of the ice-cream seller,

Behind the helter-skelter,

Past the coconut-shy.

Stop at the mound of coconuts.

Monster went to sleep here. Raspberry ran off and hid. We put a coconut in the bag.

Can you find Raspberry?

Now you are going to the river.

Start on the left by
the red rowing boat.

Paddle through lilies,

Between two crocodiles,

Under Butterfly Bridge,

Behind Monkey Island,

In front of leaping frogs,

Beneath the fishing rod,

Past the mermaid
on a rock.

Stop by the
giant seashell.

Monster went to sleep here.
Panda ran off and hid.
We put a shell in the bag.

**Can you
find Panda?**

Now you are going into the sea.

Start at the pink
and orange coral.

Go behind the crab
sitting on a rock,

Over the octopus that
lives in a ship,

Left to the large
black anchor,

Round the place where
starfish dance,

Through the waters
where striped fish swim,

Up to the pebbly beach.

**Monster went to sleep here.
Puppy ran off and hid.
We put some pebbles in the bag.**

**Can you
find Puppy?**

Now you are going into the cave.

Start at the spider
spinning a web.

Go under the brown
hanging bats,

Round the bones of
a big dinosaur,

Past a flickering lantern,

To the sleeping bears,

Down a knotted rope,

Across the stones in
a blood-red stream.

Stop at the pile
of jagged rocks.

**Monster went to sleep here.
Elly ran off and hid.
We put a rock in the bag.**

**Can you
find Elly?**

Now you are going to the mountain.

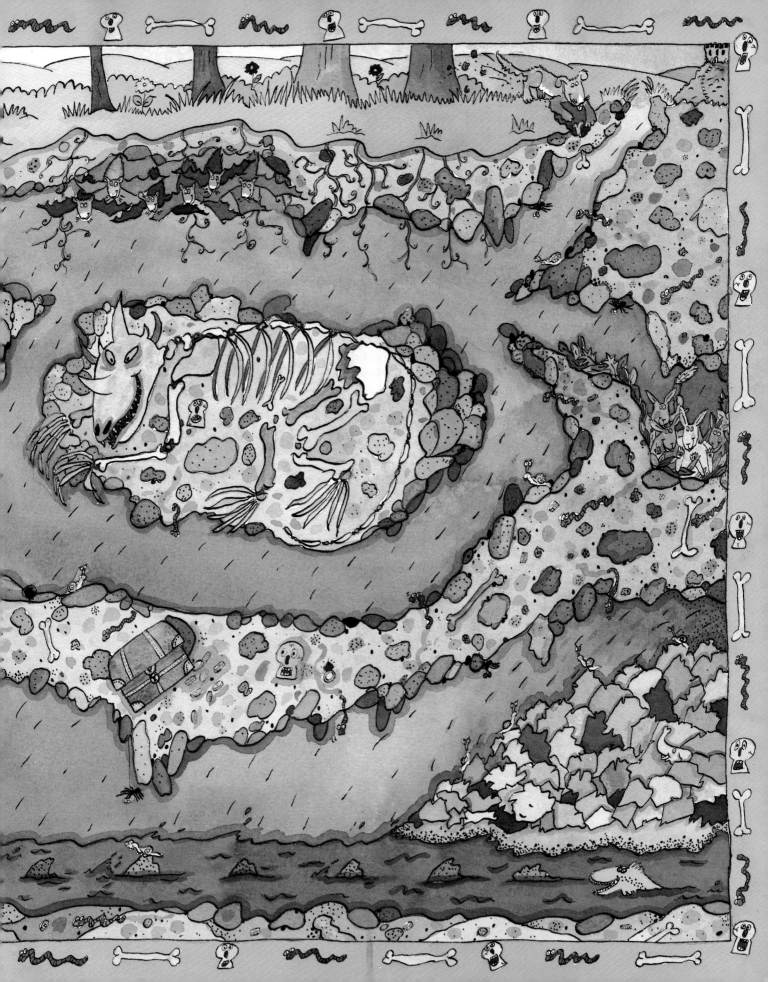

Start by the giant slimy snail.

Go past the green and nasty plants,

Between the monster flaming heads,

Under the ghastly floating ghosts,

Round a gnarled and twisted tree,

Over a bridge across a moat,

Through the rotting open door,

And into the castle at the top of

Monster Mountain!

Can you see me?

Shhh! Everyone's asleep! You must not wake them. Start at the bed with ten mini-monsters.

Go under the beastly flying bats.

Pick up the key from the guard dog's paw.

Take the rope down from its hook.

Step over the red stripy snake.

Now tie up Mighty Monster in his bed.

Unlock my door and set me free. Then take us all back home.

Go past the statue to the cosy tent. Goodbye, Rosie.

Climb up the ladder to the pretty tree-house. Goodbye, Puppy.

Go left to the stripy.cottage. Goodbye, Percy.

Find the black and white house. Goodbye, Panda.

Then go along the path to my castle. Goodbye and thank you.